Adventures in the Rainforest
Discovering Biodiversity

by Francisco Dallmeier,
Alfonso Alonso and Deanne Kloepfer

Illustrated by Sandra Glover

with additional illustrations by
Mary Ellen Didion and
Wm. Keith Harrison

The sun was just coming up Saturday morning. Ten-year-old Alina and her eight-year-old brother Julian joined Uncle Pancho in front of their home in Lima, Peru. They were very excited. Uncle Pancho had asked them to visit his field camp in the Amazon rainforest for a week!

At the camp, teams of scientists were studying biodiversity, which is all about the life of plants and animals. And Uncle Pancho promised his niece and nephew that they could help.

Alina and Julian had permission from their parents and from school to make the trip, and their classmates could hardly wait for the two to return and report on their adventures. Mr. Alonso, the science teacher, had already taught the students that biodiversity includes all living things, the genes that make each living thing different from all others and the ways that plants and animals work together.

Mr. Alonso also said that rainforests contain much of the biodiversity on Earth. They have hundreds of thousands of plant, fish, insect, reptile, amphibian, bird and mammal species. So Alina and Julian were anxious to join Uncle Pancho's scientific teams in their amazing outdoor laboratory and discover the secrets of life in the rainforest!

"Let's check the list one more time," said Uncle Pancho. Alina read as Julian looked through the items stacked outside the house. "Rubber boots. Long-sleeved shirts. Pants. Underwear. Socks. First-aid kits. Bug repellent. Flashlights, lanterns, extra batteries. Plastic water bottles. Waterproof packets for our pens, notebooks and guide books. Soap, toothbrushes, toothpaste. My camera!"

"We have tents and mosquito netting at the camp," Uncle Pancho reminded them as they loaded their things and climbed into his vehicle. "Now, I know you have lots of questions. Who wants to start?"

Julian piped up, "How do we get to the rainforest?"

"By plane," Uncle Pancho replied. He explained that their pilot, Ned, would fly them across the Andes Mountains. "We'll land on a small, dirt runway at the edge of the rainforest and take dugout canoes to the field camp."

"What is a dugout canoe?" asked Julian.

"It is a tree trunk that native people carve out and use for travel on rivers in the rainforest," said Uncle Pancho.

"What's the camp like?" Julian wanted to know.

"It's a small clearing where we set up our sleeping tents and equipment," answered his uncle. "It is also our temporary laboratory where we process specimens. Specimens are the samples of plants and animals that we collect to study and later store in museums."

"And here's the airport," he said, as he pulled in to park. "Hey, Ned!"

A tall, skinny man walked over. His t-shirt said Amazon Air Service, and the white letters on his red cap said "Working for Biodiversity."

"Hi. I'm Ned Pacheco," he smiled. "You must be Alina and Julian. First plane trip, right?"

"Yes," Alina and Julian answered together.

"Let's load your things."

It took just one trip to stow their gear in the plane. Then Alina and Julian hopped up the stairway and sat on the two seats behind the cockpit. Uncle Pancho took the co-pilot's seat.

Ned gave Alina and Julian headphone sets. "It gets very noisy in here," he explained. "You can listen to your uncle and me through the earpieces and talk to us through these mouthpieces."

"Welcome to the expedition," beamed Uncle Pancho. "You are now part of the biodiversity team!"

"Fasten your seat belts," ordered Ned. With a growing roar, the plane taxied down the runway and lifted into the blue sky.

Alina and Julian looked out the plane's window as the foothills of the Andes Mountains grew closer. Then they heard Uncle Pancho's voice in their earpieces. "Notice how the landscape changes as we go over the mountains into the rainforest," he said. "You can see the dry land conditions along the coast, then the highlands and the snowy tops of volcanoes and finally the lush green forest on the other side."

"We're crossing the Andes!" interrupted Julian. "And it's getting bumpy!"

"That's typical up here," said Ned, who had flown higher and higher until they were looking down at the craggy peaks along the crest of the Andes. "The air currents here are stronger. That's why we had to fly before 10:00 a.m. Any later and we could get caught in a storm, since clouds usually form over the Andes late in the morning," he added.

"I'm going to take a picture," said Alina, reaching for her camera.

"You know," said Uncle Pancho, "scientists use satellite pictures taken from miles above the earth to see different types of land forms, like forests and deserts." He explained that the photos also show rivers, streams, roads, farms, towns and cities. That information is helpful in remote places that scientists know little about.

"And Alina," Uncle Pancho said, "satellite photos are just one of the many tools we use to study and protect the environment. Our job is very practical. We gather scientific information about rainforest plants and animals so better decisions can be made to conserve the rainforest and biodiversity."

About an hour later, Ned announced, "We're coming to the base camp. You'll see where people are exploring for natural gas in the rainforest."

"I see a river and runway!" Julian exclaimed.

"And I see our guide Manuel and his son Daniel," said Uncle Pancho. "Daniel often comes to the field camp and helps us identify animal tracks and plants. He and his father will take us to the field camp and then return to their village. We'll visit them there at the end of the week."

After introductions, the group sat down to eat lunch. Alina and Julian immediately liked Daniel with his big grin, and Daniel was very happy to meet young people his own age. By the time everyone climbed into the motorized canoe for the trip, the three children were well on their way to becoming good friends.

Alina rode in the same canoe as her uncle. She asked him, "You mentioned specimens before. Those are the leaves and flowers you pick and the insects and other creatures you capture, right?"

"Yes," answered Uncle Pancho. "Scientists call that sampling."

"Exactly what kind of scientist are you?" Alina wanted to know.

"I'm a conservation biologist. We are sort of like doctors. You know how Dr. Mendez takes your temperature? Looks at your eyes, ears and throat? Listens to your heart? Measures your height and weight? At your next visit, she does that again and compares the new information with the old to help her decide how healthy you are."

"That's Dr. Mendez all right," Alina grinned.

Uncle Pancho explained that conservation biologists also make careful notes — where they find specimens, how they sample them, what their measurements are, whether they are adults or juveniles, male or female.

"We call that information the baseline," he said. "When we return to the same spot, we take new measurements and compare the new information with the baseline to see if there are any changes."

"It sounds like making a movie," said Alina. "You take a picture, go back for more pictures and finally put them all together to tell the story."

The canoes moved closer together as they motored further into the rainforest. From his seat in the other canoe, Julian asked, "Uncle Pancho, are rainforests more important than other environments?"

"Rainforests have a great deal of biodiversity," said Uncle Pancho thoughtfully. "But biodiversity is everywhere, even in your backyard. Remember, it includes all species, even the tiniest ones that we can see only under microscopes."

"Aren't there millions of species?" Alina asked.

"Some scientists think there may be 10 million species, while others think there might be many more!" Uncle Pancho answered. "Scientist have found about 1.8 million, and you'll see lots of them. You'll probably see more plants than animals because wild creatures are very shy around people. They usually spot us and disappear before we can see them."

Just then, Daniel pointed ahead. The field camp was coming into view around the bend!

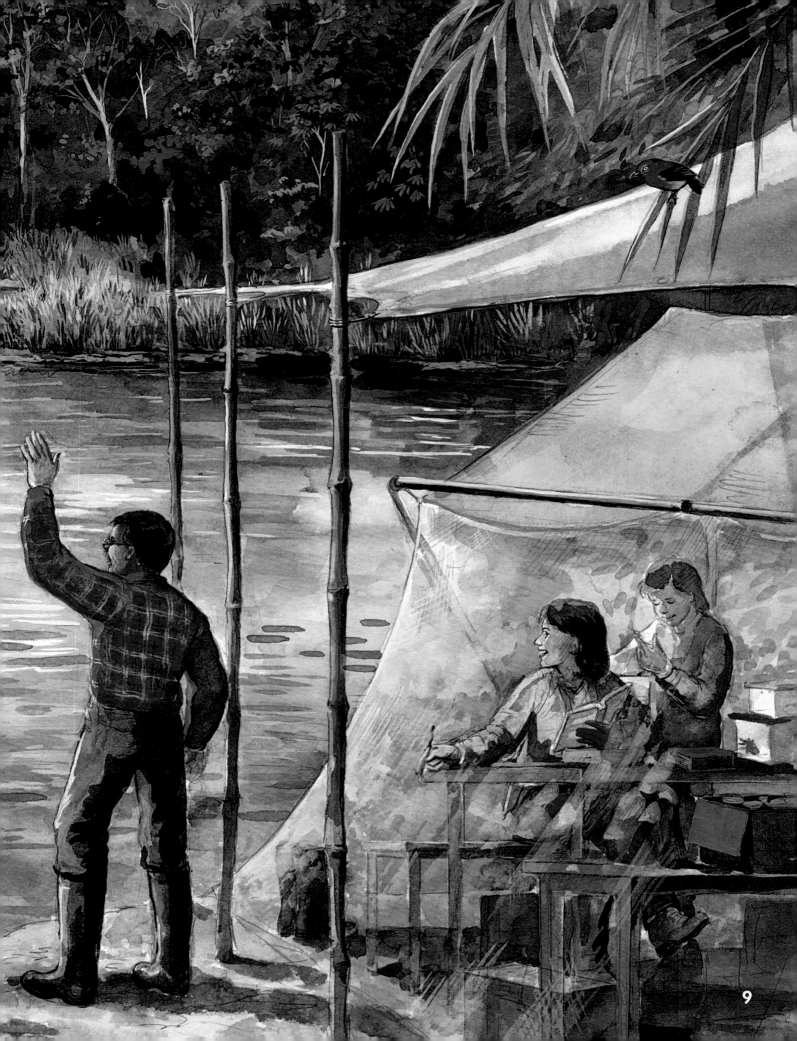

March 20

Biodiversity is all life — species, the genes that make each individual different, the ways that plants and animals interact and work together.

Conservation biologists keep track of changes in natural systems, just like family doctors do with our health.

To decide whether changes have occurred, it is important to make careful records in the field.

Scientists take specimens that are eventually stored for research and education in museums.

The information that conservation biologists gather helps us all make better decisions about conserving and using natural resources.

There are thousands, perhaps millions, of species, and we haven't even identified most of them!

Investigating Rainforest Plants

Slipper orchid

Alina and Julian rose early the next morning to join Uncle Pancho and three plant scientists, called botanists [bot-a-nists], for breakfast. On the way to the cook tent, they saw Percy, a scientist they had met the night before, already at work cutting up a rainforest fruit in the laboratory.

At the cook tent, Willy, Miguel and Rafael, the botanists, explained that they would spend the day at a research plot in the rainforest to study the various plants, which they called "vegetation."

"I can't wait!" said Alina. "Along the river yesterday, we saw so many interesting trees and flowers. I don't know how you can study them all!"

"Very carefully," laughed Rafael. He said that there are about 270,000 plant species in the world and that they have many different uses. For example, people can eat more than 50,000 plant species, but they actually use only about 150 for food. In fact, three-fourths of all humans rely on varieties of just three grains — rice, wheat and corn — for most of their food every day!

"Mr. Alonso said we get medicines from plants, too," Julian said.

Willy nodded. "Yes, and each time we find a new plant species, there is the possibility of a new food, medicine or other useful product. Remember that 30 percent of all medicines today were developed from plants and animals."

"Vegetation is more than just a lot of plant species," said Miguel. "I think of plants as building blocks that form the structure of a forest. They are like the tall and small buildings in cities that are used for homes and businesses."

He explained that in the rainforest, the taller trees form a canopy over the smaller trees and undergrowth.

Combined, the plants are habitat where many animal species live. The plants shelter the animals, and some of the animals eat different plants as their main food.

"Plants also help hold the soil together so that it won't run off into streams and rivers during rainstorms," said Willy. "This is important because too much runoff can destroy fish habitat. Also, decaying plants add ingredients to the soil that make it healthier so other vegetation grows better."

"Have an exciting day with the botanists!" exclaimed Uncle Pancho. "Your lunches are in your backpacks. I'll see you back here for dinner."

And Alina and Julian followed the botanists and Juan, the local guide, down a narrow trail leading to the research plot deep in the rainforest.

Tropical flowers

"Look at that flower over there!" Julian exclaimed.

"That plant with the bright red flowers? It looks like a *Heliconia standleyi* [hel–i–cone-ee-uh stand-lee-eye]," said Willy. "As you can see, it's a favorite of hummingbirds because it produces lots of nectar."

"That is a strange name for a flower," said Julian.

"It's a Latin name," replied Rafael. He said Latin is the language many European scientists used a long time ago to name species. "We still use Latin today so that there is a single scientific name for each species that all scientists can recognize," he added.

Rafael took a sample flower and leaf from the plant to compare with the reference books at camp. "Alina, look at those spines!" Julian pointed to a spiky plant.

"Plants protect themselves in many ways," Willy observed. "Those spines keep animals from climbing and eating the plants."

And some plants, Rafael explained, are homes for insects such as aggressive ants, whose bites and stings are painful. In exchange for a home, the ants protect the plants from being eaten by insects and other creatures.

Plant spines

"One interesting thing about this work is learning how plants and animals work together," said Miguel. "Like that hummingbird we just saw. It carries pollen from flower to flower as it drinks nectar. Pollen helps the plants produce fruits, which carry the seeds to grow more plants."

When the team arrived at the spot where the research plot was located, Alina looked puzzled. "How do you know where the plot is in the middle of all these trees and other plants?" she asked.

"When we choose a place for a plot, we mark it with stakes," answered Miguel. "Most of the stakes at this plot are hidden by plants that have grown since we set up this plot three years ago. But we made a map and took careful notes so we could find the trees in the plot on future trips."

"Now," Willy said, "we can measure to see how much those trees have grown, and we'll also check for any new plants and dead ones."

"Our plots are one hectare in size," said Miguel. "That's about the size of two and a half football fields. After we mark the boundaries, we divide the hectare into 25 smaller units. That makes it easier to identify each plant in all parts of the plot."

Willy said that they measure all trees with a special tape that records the diameter. Each tree that is at least four centimeters (about 1.5 inches) in diameter at 1.3 meters (about four feet) off the ground gets its own special number. The smaller trees are not measured.

"Julian, will you help us re-measure the diameter of this mahogany tree?" asked Willy.

"It's 17.6 centimeters," Julian responded. "Did you get that, Alina?"

"Yes," said his sister. "According to the notes, it has grown two centimeters in three years."

Tropical tree trunk

Bromeliad

"Thanks," said Miguel. "Oh, see that tree over there on the ground?" he pointed. "The notes say it was standing when we first studied the plot."

"Why did it fall down?" asked Alina.

"That's what we have to decide," said Miguel. "Maybe a big wind knocked it over, or it might have died from old age. See the rotted out core? It's a very old tree."

"We'll take some more samples of leaves and flowers," said Willy. "And Rafael is on his way up that tree over there to sample high in the canopy where many plants live that are not found down here."

Miguel looked through his binoculars and exclaimed, "I think that's a bromeliad [bro-me-lee-ad] canopy plant Rafael is after! Binoculars are very useful in identifying leaf shapes, flowers and fruits up in the canopy."

"We also pay attention to the color of plants and the way the tree sap smells," added Miguel. "That helps us figure out which group of plants we are studying."

"How did you decide where to place the plots?" Alina wanted to know.

"We started with satellite photographs," said Willy.

"Uncle Pancho told us that scientists use those," said Julian.

"They were helpful here," Willy continued. "They showed us the canopy, river systems and a little about what kind of species we might find."

"After that, we figured out which kind of plant species is likely to exist in the area, and we studied the area's geography, topography and geology," said Miguel. "Then we chose where to locate the plots. We usually select areas that we think show what will be found throughout a larger region."

"Are all the plant species in the bigger area found in a single plot?" asked Alina.

"Many, but not all," answered Miguel. "We might have to conduct a special study for some uncommon species."

"Then why use plots?" Alina wondered.

"To understand how the forest is structured," replied Willy. "That means where species are located in relation to each other, how different they are from each other and how they interact."

"There's so much to learn," sighed Alina.

"Yes," laughed Willy. "Back at camp, we'll enter everything we learned today into the computer so others can use that knowledge!"

Alina's and Julian's Camp Journal

March 21

Trees and other plants are the building blocks of forests. They create habitat for other plants and animals.

The rainforest usually has three vegetation levels: a canopy with the tallest trees, an understory and ground cover.

The roots of plants anchor the plants to the ground and provide them with water and nutrients. Roots also stop soil from running off into streams.

Plots are important to record accurate information about plants and other living things and to check them from time to time. Scientists call this process "monitoring."

Species in plots must be carefully measured and recorded so that scientists can tell if changes have taken place over time and where.

Each species has a special Latin name — not just the plants, but all living things that scientists have discovered.

Learning about Aquatic Systems

The next morning, the two children met Norma, Raul, Pedro and Max — the aquatic scientists — and headed to a stream winding its way through the rainforest. They were going to gather information about the quality of the water and the number and different kinds of species that live there.

"Will we get a chance to fish?" asked Julian hopefully.

"Yes, but not with a pole," said Raul. "We use nets to sample fish and other interesting life forms in streams and rivers. We'll show you how we take the samples, and then you can help."

"There's more to this than just fishing!" Norma added with a smile. "We measure the temperature of the water and the speed of the current. And we take samples of the water at different points along the rivers and streams to test it."

She explained that these measurements are some of the vital signs that tell scientists how the river or stream is doing. And she said that clean water and healthy water systems are necessary for life. If the quality of the water starts to decrease, it could harm many species, including humans.

"Let's get started," said Max. "Pedro and Raul are going downstream to sample at other stations. Norma and I will show you how we work."

First, he took the temperature of the water and made notes before pulling several small bottles from his pack. He then crossed to the center of the stream, filled the bottles with water and capped them. As he waded back to shore, he handed the samples to the young people.

"Hold these, will you?" he asked, climbing up the bank to record the date, time and location in his notebook. He also noted how wide and how fast the water was running in the stream. Next, he took a special kit from his pack and reached for one of the full bottles.

"I'm going to measure the oxygen level in the water," he explained.

Max said that most plants, insects and animals that spend all or part of their life cycles in water need some oxygen to survive. If too much soil or too much waste gets into the water, the oxygen is lost, and some species may no longer be able to live in the water.

Dragonfly larva

"We also measure the pH, which is the hydrogen level. We measure it between 0 and 14," said Norma. "Drinking water should have a pH of about 7."

"This stream has a pH of 7.5 and a temperature of 24 degrees Celsius, which is not too hot or too cold," stated Max. "It looks healthy! Now, let's get the hand nets and see how many different kinds of organisms we can sample. There should be a lot of insects. We need samples from ten different spots to complete our work, and we'll probably find different species at each location."

After watching for a few minutes, Alina and Julian began putting nets into the stream.

"Look!" Alina called. "I caught a strange bug."

"That's a very young dragonfly," said Max, after examining the creature. "It likes lots of oxygen in water."

"Don't dragonflies live in the air?" asked Julian.

"Not at first," Norma responded. "They deposit their eggs in the water, and the larvae live there before becoming full-fledged dragonflies."

Then Norma told Alina and Julian to hold their nets deep in the stream against the current and kick at the streambed. When they brought their nets to the surface, each held insects that had been hiding among the pebbles and mud at the bottom of the stream.

"Excellent," said Norma. "Put those samples into a tray and label it number one for this creek. Then we need to sort out the insects from the pebbles and dead leaves. Insects are easier to see while they're still moving. We'll sort again back at camp, where we can also examine these specimens under the microscope."

"Look, this one has three tails!" exclaimed Julian.

"I see that," said Norma. "It belongs to the group Trichoptera [tri-chop-ter-a], and it also likes water with lots of oxygen and minerals like nitrates. So do the members of the group Ephemeroptera [e-fem-er-op-ter-a], which are organisms that live in the water most of their lives. When they become adults, they fly away from the water and live for only one or two days."

Fishfly larva

Mayfly larva

Caddisfly larva

As the group finished sorting, Pedro and Raul joined them with their own samples from further downstream. The scientists then took a wide net out of one of the backpacks, and Pedro and Raul waded into the water. They stretched the net and quickly pulled it along, while holding it close to the bottom of the stream. After a few minutes, everyone helped pull the net up on shore and then began dumping the fish and insects into buckets that were filled with water from the stream.

"Wow!" exclaimed Julian. "Look at these fish. It would take me all day to catch this many with my fishing rod."

The scientists measured the fish after they finished separating out the insects. As they worked, Raul explained the different roles that fish play.

He said that the streams in this part of the rainforest have fishes such as catfish that feed at the bottom of the river, among mud and pebbles, while other fish species prefer the middle depth of the river, and still others live closer to the surface.

"Bottom feeders eat algae and organic material like dead leaves or rotted fish," added Pedro. "Some grow quite large and are a favorite source of protein for people in the villages. Your friend Daniel has told us the native names for many of the fish around here."

"Maybe we'll have a fish dinner with Daniel's family when we go to his village," smiled Alina.

"Many fish species eat aquatic insects," Norma said, "or fruits that fall into the streams. Some fish eat other fish. And some, like the piranha, eat animals that swim in the water. Piranhas are small, but they will attack even large mammals — including humans!"

March 22

In this rainforest, healthy, safe water has a pH of about 7.5 and a temperature of about 24 degrees Celsius.

It is important to check the vital signs of streams and rivers on a regular basis to make sure the water is healthy.

Today, we found more than 60 different species of aquatic insects.

About 22,000 fish species have been identified around the world. So far in this part of the rainforest, the scientists have identified 125 fish species.

Fish are an important source of protein for the villagers.

Exploring for Invertebrates

Bright and early, Alina and Julian joined Uncle Pancho, Saida, Maria and José — the team's entomologists [en-to-mol-o-gists]. They study insects. The group hiked to a different research plot to sample Uncle Pancho's favorite creatures — bugs.

"We'll be focusing on invertebrates," said Saida. "I heard you found some yesterday at the stream."

"What exactly are invertebrates?" asked Julian.

"Like all insects, they have no backbones or spinal columns, and they are among the smallest and most common creatures on Earth. They include butterflies, flies, bees, beetles, earthworms, plant bugs, spiders, scorpions, mites, crabs, crayfishes, lobsters and lots more."

"Alina," said José, "your uncle told me that you are interested in invertebrates and already know quite a bit about them."

"I don't," said Julian. "Why are they so special?"

Maria spoke up. "First of all, there are more invertebrates than any other group. Scientists have identified about 900,000 insect species, which is more than half of all species known at this time. They live in almost every environment."

Termites

"My favorites are the beetles," added Uncle Pancho. "Two-thirds of all the insect species we know about are beetles. That's 600,000 beetle species!"

"And invertebrates perform a lot of different services," said José. He explained that some, such as bees, pollinate plants just like the hummingbird that Julian and Alina saw two days before. Others such as butterfly caterpillars and leaf-cutter ants feed on plants. Ants also disperse the seeds of plants by carrying them to their nests.

"Even earthworms are important," said Maria. "They tunnel through the soil and let air in, and they move the soil around and loosen it up, which helps keep it healthy. Invertebrates are also important as food. Many other animals love to eat them, and even some plants consume insects. In fact, invertebrates are the favorite food for many birds, reptiles, amphibians, fishes and mammals."

"It sounds like the more you learn about invertebrates, the more you learn about how nature works," said Alina.

Fungi are decomposers.

Leaf-cutter ant

29

"Right," said Uncle Pancho. "There are so many, and they do so many different things that the information we gather about them is very helpful to understand how nature's systems work. We have many ways to sample them."

"I like to use my bug net," smiled Alina.

"Yes. We can also just turn over leaves and find them on the ground or use traps like this pitfall trap," Uncle Pancho said, pointing to a cup buried in the ground. "I set it up a few days ago."

"As you can see, it is fairly simple," he explained. "It's just a plastic cup set in a hole. The top of the cup is level with the ground. Crawling insects fall into the cup, which contains a preserving solution that is a form of alcohol. I placed a little tent over the cup to protect it from the rain."

"This trap caught several invertebrates," said Alina. "I see a spider, some ants and a beetle."

Pitfall trap

"We'll collect them in a flask and label it with the trap number and date. You can help us examine them under the microscope tonight," said Uncle Pancho.

"For bait in the traps, we use several kinds of food that invertebrates eat, including decayed fruit or rotting meat and fish, to attract different kinds of insects," said Saida. "We also use yellow pan traps because several insect species are attracted to yellow. We set the pan traps in the ground and fill them with soapy water, which causes insects to sink faster. The insects are trapped once they fall into the solution."

"We also use malaise traps," said Uncle Pancho.

"What are those?" asked Julian.

"They are nets with a fine mesh that catch flying insects," answered his uncle. "You will see how we hang them on branches or place them on the ground. Once in the net, the insects tend to move up toward the sunlight filtering through the top, where we have a chamber containing a preserving solution. When they enter the chamber, the insects fall into the solution. We carefully remove the specimens and take them back to camp."

"Wow! You must get lots of specimens with those traps," exclaimed Julian.

"Yes," said Maria. "And as we return to camp, watch for army ants marching along the forest floor!"

Malaise trap

Army ants

31

After dinner back at camp, Uncle Pancho explained that the greatest challenge in studying invertebrates is the lab work. The scientists first identify the specimens by comparing them to pictures and descriptions of known species in reference books. Then, they put the specimens back in solutions to prevent spoilage, carefully label them and transport them to other laboratories or museums for permanent storage and display.

"It takes a lot of time to make sense of all the information the specimens provide," said Uncle Pancho. "But it is important because that information helps answer questions about how nature works and whether humans are disrupting nature's cycles. We use that information to assist people in making decisions that are better for the environment."

"Now come look through this microscope," said José, "and I'll show you that all bugs do not look alike!"

"I see what you mean," said Alina. "I thought these two spiders were the same, but one is a different shade of brown and has a different shape to its abdomen."

"Before you start having too much fun with the microscope, I want you to join me for some night-time sampling," said Uncle Pancho. "Many invertebrates are most active at night, and I think you'll be interested in how we catch them."

"You bet!" exclaimed the young people, and they trooped out of the tent behind their uncle.

Soon they came to a white sheet hanging from the trees. A purple light powered by a strong portable battery lit up the sheet. Hundreds of insects — moths, wasps, beetles, ants and others

Forest insects

32

— attracted by the light had landed or were crawling on the sheet.

"What a variety," breathed Alina.

"Look!" said Julian. "That praying mantis is having a midnight snack."

"And I think I hear some frogs that also want to feast!" laughed Uncle Pancho as he and the children carefully gathered several insects into jars filled with preserving solution.

"You'll get a chance to catch frogs tomorrow night," he added as they walked back to camp. "First, off to bed. And I need to go back to the lab for a few hours."

33

March 23

There are more insect species on Earth than all other species combined!

We saw a lot of them — different sizes, shapes, colors and kinds.

Insects are invertebrates. They have no backbones. They clean up decaying matter, make tunnels in the soil so air can circulate and are food for many animals.

Scientists spend many hours in the lab. They don't sleep very much!

Looking for Frogs and Snakes

By eight o'clock the next morning, Alina and Julian were on their way to look for amphibians (frogs, toads, salamanders) and reptiles (lizards, snakes, turtles) with Javier and Eliana, the herpetologists [her-pe-tol-o-gists] on the team. As they walked, the scientists explained that amphibians and reptiles are important as both predators (hunters) and prey (food) in maintaining nature's balance.

"Eliana, what is the difference between amphibians and reptiles?" asked Julian.

Eliana said that both are vertebrates, which means they have backbones or spinal columns, and both can live in water and on land. Both are also cold-blooded, which means their body temperature is about the same as the air temperature around them. But unlike reptiles, amphibians are born in water and have gills as tadpoles. When they migrate to land, they develop lungs. And amphibians do not have scales, while most reptiles do.

"Amphibians help warn us when the environment is no longer healthy," added Javier. "They have very thin, sensitive skin. If there are changes in the quality of the water or air, the animals are likely to get sick fairly quickly or die off."

"Amphibian populations around the world are declining," said Eliana. "We think our work here will uncover some of the reasons and some solutions."

"What will we see today?" asked Julian.

"We're going to a marsh, where we might see caimans, which are like alligators, and frogs or maybe one or two species of turtles," said Javier. "We'll also go to a gap in the forest that was created when a large tree fell down. We should see lizards there. The sun helps warm them as they hunt."

"Will we see different things in the gap from what we saw in the part of the rainforest that we visited with the plant team?" Alina asked.

"Good question," replied Javier. "The answer is yes. Some of the plants and animals in the gap will be different from those you observed at the shady plot under the closed tree canopy." He went on to explain that lots of people think rainforests are filled with the same kinds of plant and animal species throughout. But most are made up of many habitats populated by different plants and animals. As an example, Javier said that some fish in small, shaded, fast-moving streams cannot survive in nearby larger, slow-moving rivers with more sunlight.

Eliana suddenly turned as they neared the forest gap and motioned to the rest of the group to join her quietly.

"See that?"

A lizard resting on a small log in the forest gap looked up alertly and snatched an insect flying by, then disappeared into the surrounding plant growth.

"That was exciting!" said Javier as they moved into the gap. "Wildlife is very difficult to spot, as you know. Now, let's see what we find in the leaf bed on the forest floor."

"We mark off an area that is 5 by 5 meters square, or approximately 15 feet on each side, and sift through the leaf litter," explained Eliana. "Put on your gloves. We might turn up some snakes, so stay back until we say it is safe."

Just then Javier exclaimed, "Look at this!" as he held up a long brownish-yellow and white snake called Imantodes cenchoa [i-mant-odes cen-cho-a]. "It's not poisonous, so come over for a closer look. We are quite lucky. Snakes are hard to find in the rainforest because most of them are active at night."

"Lucky? I don't know about that," mumbled Julian as he and Alina approached the snake.

"Hey," said Alina, "this snake is really neat up close. I think you just have to get used to them."

Ground snake

"How do you catch lizards?" Julian wondered. "They move so fast."

"There are several ways," answered Javier. "Some scientists use sticky traps. After an animal attaches itself to the trap, the scientists apply oil to remove it. We also look for amphibians and reptiles in their hideouts — in tree holes and in the ground."

"Let's move over and check the drift fence," said Eliana. "That's one of my favorite ways to sample."

"What is it?" asked Julian.

"It's a fence-like structure that we place on the forest floor," Eliana explained. "When animals bump up against it, they often follow it until they fall into the bucket we set at the end of the fence. We use large buckets buried in the soil with the top of the bucket at ground level."

"Time to finish up and return to camp," said Javier. "We need to start processing these specimens in the lab. And don't forget! This evening, we're going to see if any frogs are out and about."

At about 7:00 p.m., the team came to a small stream. It had been raining for a couple hours. Everyone had on rain gear, and they wore headlamps. The scientists carried tape recorders and plastic bags in case they caught any frogs.

"Rainy weather is ideal for sampling frogs," smiled Javier from under his rain hat. "Once again, we're lucky. We should see some frogs and hear lots of songs to help us identify species that usually do not sing on dry nights."

"Listen," said Eliana. "I think I hear a tree frog, probably an Agalychnis craspedopus [ag-a-lick-nis cras-ped-o-pus]."

Javier recorded the song and played it back. The tree frog responded vigorously and from closer than before.

"It sounds like there is a frog over that way," Julian whispered. "Can I try to catch it?"

"Yes," answered Javier quietly, "but remember to move slowly and make no noise. When you get close to the frog, move your hands quickly."

"Wow, I got it!" shouted Julian a few minutes later.

"Good work," smiled Eliana.

On the way back to camp, Alina saw a large snake crossing the path. "Look! Is that a friendly snake?" she asked, pointing.

"Don't move!" ordered Javier. "That's one of the largest bushmasters I have ever seen!"

"They are very poisonous," shuddered Eliana. "I'm glad it's moving away! Their venom helps them survive by paralyzing their prey and also their predators. I don't want this one to think we are enemies!"

"It's a good idea to look carefully at snakes to keep safe, but also to keep them safe," said Javier. "Many non-poisonous snakes are killed by people when they confuse them with poisonous ones."

At camp, the scientists said good night and went immediately to work in the lab for a few more hours. They sorted and photographed the specimens carefully and entered their field notes into computers.

Alina and Julian, asleep in their tents, dreamed of frogs, toads and snakes.

Frog specimens

41

Alina's and Julian's Camp Journal

March 24

There are about 12,000 known species of amphibians and reptiles in the world.

Amphibians and reptiles are both cold-blooded vertebrates that live on land and in water. The differences are that amphibians are born in water and go through a tadpole stage before maturing and moving to land where they develop lungs. Reptiles do not. And reptiles have scales, but amphibians don't.

Frogs, toads, salamanders and newts are common amphibians.

Snakes, alligators, crocodiles, lizards and turtles are common reptiles.

Amphibians and reptiles work with other species to maintain nature's balance in the rainforest.

Keeping track of (monitoring) amphibians is very important. They warn us when things go wrong in the environment.

Surveying Birds

Tatiana, Constantino, Antonio and Edwin — the team's bird specialists (called ornithologists [or-ni-thol-o-gists]) — woke the young people at 4:30 a.m. before the sun rose. It was still quite dark as they grabbed some bananas from the cook tent and began their journey.

"We need to get an early start because many birds are most active at dawn," explained Tatiana.

"Our team uses binoculars, tape recorders, cameras and mist nets for bird counts," said Constantino. "We set up ten mist nets two days ago, and as you will see, we are still catching lots of birds. Edwin is going ahead now to open the nets."

As they walked through the forest, Julian said, "Uncle Pancho told us that we must be especially quiet today."

"Yes," answered Tatiana. "Birds are difficult to see in the rainforest, and they are easily disturbed by strange noises."

"Alina and Julian," whispered Antonio as he stopped and pointed, "look through your binoculars at that branch. Can you see the green toucan?"

"Yes," the children whispered back. "It has a very large beak," said Alina, "and I think it's eating something."

"That's a fig tree, and toucans really like its fruit," Tatiana replied.

"Toucans, parrots and macaws prefer fruits. Other species of birds like different things to eat," explained Constantino as the group moved on. He said that some birds eat only leaves, while others follow army ants and eat

Yellow-tufted woodpecker

the insects that the ants scare up. Some birds feed only on the invertebrates that live in bamboo, and others such as swallows, warblers and woodpeckers also eat insects.

"What about hawks?" asked Alina.

"Hawks, eagles and other raptors feed on birds, mammals, amphibians, reptiles and fish," said Constantino. "One of the most impressive is the harpy eagle. It eats monkeys."

"Wow! That must be a big bird," Julian said.

"The harpy eagle is one of the largest of the rainforest birds that look for prey as they fly above the canopy," Tatiana said. "And don't forget about the roles that birds play." She told Alina and Julian that fruit-eating birds such as toucans deposit seeds in their droppings. In fact, some seeds won't sprout unless they have passed through the acids in a bird's digestive system! Other species such as hummingbirds feed on nectar and pollinate plants, just like bees. And still others eat enough insects to help control insect populations.

"And just like us, birds need mineral supplements," said Tatiana. "We often see flocks of macaws and other parrots eating clay from river cliffs to get salt."

"There's Edwin," Constantino pointed ahead.

"You're just in time," Edwin welcomed the group. "Shortly after I opened the nets, several birds flew into them. I need your help to bag, measure, photograph and band the birds before we release them."

As the group moved closer, Alina said excitedly, "I see a colorful yellow and green bird with a blue head!"

"A blue-crowned motmot," said Tatiana.

In all, there were six birds in the mist net, which was made from fine mesh and strung between two poles 3 to 4 meters (9 to 12 feet) high.

The young people watched as Tatiana and Constantino carefully removed the birds from the net and placed them in loosely tied cloth bags. Then they took the birds out, one at a time. The youngsters helped measure wings and bodies, and Tatiana made notes and took pictures. Just before releasing each bird, Edwin placed a numbered ring on one of its legs.

"If we catch these birds again at this station or somewhere else, we'll know from the band that they have already been measured, and we will also know something about their movements," Tatiana said.

"And now, we're going to do what is called point counts. We walk on a trail for about 50 meters, or approximately 160 feet, and then stop to listen for bird songs for about ten minutes. Then we move on to the next point."

At the first point, the group heard no birds. At the second, they sat down, and Edwin turned on the tape recorder. A few minutes later, they heard a bird singing. Edwin recorded the song and played it back.

While they waited for a response, the young people heard early morning noises of the rainforest — rustlings in the undergrowth as small creatures scurried away and the sounds of many insects.

Suddenly a song rang out from high overhead. They peered through their binoculars as the song grew louder.

"What is that colorful bird?" asked Alina.

"A male manakin. You can tell by his bright red head, yellow belly and black wings," said Tatiana. "This is our first count of a manakin!"

Blue-crowned motmot

"Speaking of counting," grinned Julian, "how many bird species are there?"

"We know of about 10,000 so far," Constantino smiled in return. "In this part of the rainforest, we have recorded more than 500. That makes this one of the richest areas for bird species anywhere in the world!"

"Time to return to camp," announced Tatiana. "We need to start entering all of this information into the computers and get ready for the night search."

As they walked back, Antonio said, "I'm anxious to listen to the recordings. I'm pretty sure I heard some songs from birds that we didn't actually see." He put on his headset and listened carefully for several minutes, then exclaimed, "Yes! We didn't see any rufous-breasted piculets [ru-fus brest-ed pick-u-lets] or semi-collared puffbirds, but their songs are on the tape!"

Constantino took the headset and listened too. "Great, Antonio. Alina and Julian, that's why it is so important to use different sampling methods. We never know what we will learn!"

Tiger heron

That evening, the group gathered again and put on their headlamps to search for birds that are active at night. After walking a good distance from the field camp, they arrived at a point and turned off their lamps. Antonio started the tape recorder and played short bursts of owl hoots.

Alina, resting against a tree trunk, suddenly realized that the hooting was no longer coming from the tape but from the branch of a nearby tree. She listened closely as did the rest of the team. Then Tatiana motioned to the others to turn on their headlamps. When they did, they saw the reflection of two red eyes.

"That's a potoo [pu-too]," whispered Antonio. "It is a fascinating species that we know very little about. What we do know is that this bird eats insects, perches upright without moving on tree branches and is almost impossible to detect during the day."

At the next point, the taped calls attracted spectacled and crested owls. "An extremely satisfying day and night!" Tatiana proclaimed as the group returned to camp.

"And I'm exhausted," said Alina. Her brother yawned in agreement.

49

March 25

Birds are important to spread seeds, pollinate flowers and control the populations of insects and other animals.

We used mist nets, point counts, direct sightings and tape-recorded bird songs to count birds.

Many of the bird species in the mist nets were from the middle and lower heights in the rainforest canopy.

Banding the birds helps scientists monitor their movements and decide if the populations are steady.

We recorded owl songs and saw the eyes of a potoo at night.

Seeking
Mammals

"Meet Jessica, Sergio and Major," said Uncle Pancho at breakfast the next day. "Major is from the United States."

"Welcome to the team," smiled Jessica.

"Are you ready to study mammals?" asked Major.

"Yes," answered Julian, "and I already know something about them. They drink milk from their mothers and have hair on their bodies. So that means humans are mammals."

"Correct. There are about 4,600 known species of mammals," explained Sergio, "and most of them are very difficult to observe. They have tremendous senses of smell, sight and hearing, so they almost always detect us before we see them. That makes our work much more interesting. We have to play private investigator and learn about them mostly through the signs they leave."

"Will we see any that nobody has studied before?" asked Alina.

"Maybe," said Jessica. "Even if we don't, there are plenty of known species here — like monkeys, bats, sloths, deer, anteaters, mice and jaguars."

She explained that just like other groups of living things in the rainforest, mammals have many different jobs. A large number of them feed on leaves or fruits and deposit plant seeds in their droppings. That helps plants grow throughout the habitat of the animal. Some mammals eat insects and other animals, including mammals.

Jessica also said that bats are a special group of mammals. They are able to fly and are very important in the rainforest. She promised they would look for bats that night.

As the team headed down a trail, Major talked about different ways to sample mammals. "We use scent posts and baited traps for most species and mist nets for bats at night. We also look for tracks, bones, hair and other signs," he said. "Sometimes we set up a camera that snaps photos when an animal trips the infrared sensor on the way to one of our lures."

"What are scent posts?" Alina wondered.

"Cotton balls that we cover with scents made from animal glands. These smells are very attractive to different animals," said Sergio. "When they come to sniff the scent, the animals leave tracks and other signs like scratch marks on trees or even their droppings, which we call scat."

Major said that a lot can be learned from signs. An ocelot's scat, for example, might contain bone fragments or hairs from animals it ate or maybe seeds from plants it ingested.

"Oh," said Julian, clearly uncertain whether he wanted to study scat. "How do you choose the best places to set the traps?" he asked, changing the subject.

"We know about the favorite habitats of rainforest mammals from our own experience, from what other people like your friend, Daniel, tell us and from reference books," answered Jessica.

Tayra

Jaguarundi

Bush dog

"Daniel must know a lot about rainforest animals. I can't wait to talk with him again!" said Alina as the group arrived at the scent posts, set out the day before. Major motioned for the young people to stay back while he carefully looked over the ground for tracks, hair and other signs.

Then Sergio showed Alina and Julian how to measure tracks and pointed out that different shapes represent different species.

Major said, "These prints look like those of a bush dog, and that is consistent with the scent we used. Sometimes the scents excite the animals so much that they roll around in the dirt. I see some hairs here where an animal obviously was rolling. They are also probably from a bush dog. We'll examine them under the microscope later."

"Let's take a short hike along the stream," said Sergio, "and then head back to camp along a different trail."

As the group walked, Jessica stopped to measure a track.

"I think this belongs to a tapir," she said. "Tapirs are rainforest creatures that look like a cross between a pig and an elephant. Actually, they are related to horses."

Neotropical otter

55

After dinner and just as dark was falling — when bats in the Amazon rainforest are most active — the mammal team visited the spots where Sergio had earlier placed six mist nets, just like those the bird team used. He located three over a watering hole because, as he explained, "Bats are usually thirsty when they come out at night." He set the other nets directly across a path where the scientists knew bats went to find insects. It was also near a group of fig trees where Jessica had seen fruit-eating bats before.

"Do the nets hurt the birds and bats?" asked Julian.

"No. It's like being caught in a spider web," said Major. "And we are very careful when we take the bats and birds out of the nets. We keep some of the bats as specimens and release the others after measuring and tagging them."

At the watering hole, the scientists put on gloves and pulled out their cloth bags. Julian and Alina could see that seven bats were caught in the net. The team approached with their headlamps on, and Sergio began putting the bats in the bags.

Fish-eating bat

Fruit-eating bat

Frog-eating bat

"We have quite a variety here," said Sergio as he measured each bat and Alina shined her lamp on a notebook to record the measurements. "This vampire bat is called Vampyrum spectrum [vam-pie-rum spec-trum]. It is the largest bat on the South American continent, and its favorite meal is frogs and mice. That one with the long tail, named Tadarida brasiliensis [tad-a-ree-da braz-il-en-sis], eats insects, and this stinky one called Noctilio leporinus [noc-til-ee-o lep-or-I-nus] eats fish."

Later at the mist nets across the trail, the team waited for nearly an hour, but no bats appeared. Normally, they would have seen insect-, fruit- and nectar-eating bats.

"Sometimes that happens," said Sergio. But as he was about to continue talking, Major stopped him. "Listen!" From somewhere fairly nearby came a cat-like scream.

"Jaguar!" exclaimed Jessica. "And too close for comfort. Time to go back to camp!"

57

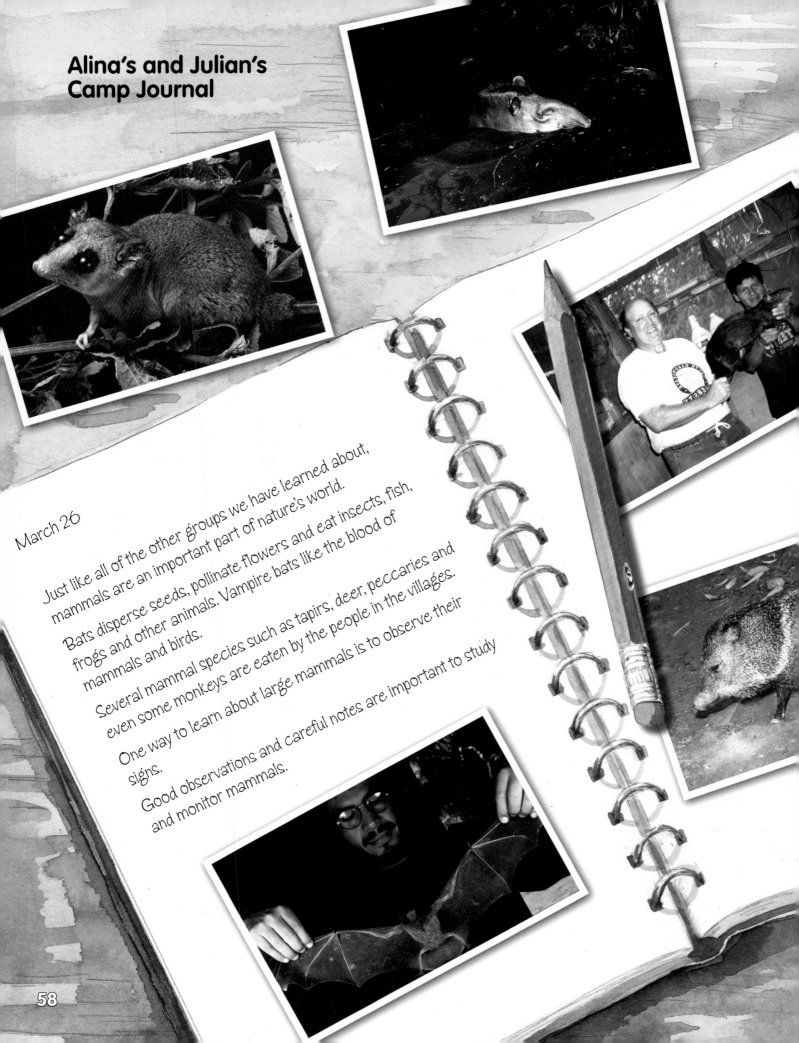

Alina's and Julian's Camp Journal

March 26

Just like all of the other groups we have learned about, mammals are an important part of nature's world.

Bats disperse seeds, pollinate flowers and eat insects, fish, frogs and other animals. Vampire bats like the blood of mammals and birds.

Several mammal species such as tapirs, deer, peccaries and even some monkeys are eaten by the people in the villages.

One way to learn about large mammals is to observe their signs.

Good observations and careful notes are important to study and monitor mammals.

Collared aracaris

Sharing Biodiversity Stories

Preparing
cassava bread

On their last day in the rainforest, Alina and Julian rose early to thank the scientists, cooks and camp crew. They walked with Uncle Pancho to where Daniel and Manuel were waiting with the canoes to take them to the village and immediately began to tell Daniel about their adventures. Sergio and Norma went along because they were also going in the plane the next day to take equipment and specimens back to Lima.

As soon as the canoes touched land at the village, Daniel jumped out and ran toward a woman and other children standing nearby.

"That's my wife Lucia," said Manuel, "and Daniel's brother and sisters."

"Which house is yours?" asked Alina.

Manuel pointed. "Over there. You can see that we make our homes from rainforest trees and plants. We also use forest vegetation to make spears, tools and household goods such as baskets. We trade some of them with merchants who visit the village. We also trade crops we grow, like cacao and a green vegetable called achiote [ack-ee-oh-tay]. Come meet Lucia. She can show you where to put your things."

"Mama is one of the instructors for basket making in the village," said Daniel proudly.

"Thank you, Daniel. And now, please show your guests around the village," Lucia said, smiling at her son.

"Okay. Follow me."

As they walked, Alina said, "Daniel, I'm curious. What native group do you belong to?"

"My people are Machiguenga [Ma-chi-huen-ga]. We have lived here for many, many years. We are very traditional and, like Papa said, we rely on the rainforest for most of our needs. We live in small villages and hunt and fish for food, but we also grow some crops, and we raise chickens and other animals. We make all our own bread from the manioc [man-ee-ock] plant's starchy roots, which we crush by hand."

"And now I have a question," he smiled. "I told my friends and the adults in the village that you would share what you have learned with us. Will you?"

"We'd love to!" shouted Alina and Julian enthusiastically. "Uncle Pancho, Norma and Sergio can help!"

By early afternoon, Alina, Julian and the scientists had arranged their equipment, specimens and reference books in an open-sided meeting hut. The villagers gathered around as the group took turns describing a mist net, pitfall traps, scent posts and other equipment.

The villagers were especially interested in the specimens that Alina and Julian showed. They supplied local names and asked where the scientists took the samples. Many of the children and adults gave advice on where other plants and animals might be found.

Norma demonstrated how the scientists use the tape recorder to register the songs of birds and frogs and then play them back. Several children squealed with delight when she played the owl hoots.

Sergio spoke about the importance of accurately identifying each species and how the reference books and knowledge of local people are helpful in making those identifications. He said he was very pleased to learn so much about rainforest biodiversity from the villagers.

Alina demonstrated a laptop computer and explained how the scientists enter the data they gather to keep precise records of their discoveries. At Manuel's request, Uncle Pancho described how the scientists preserve specimens and explained that the specimens would be placed in museums in Peru, in the collections of some of Peru's universities and possibly in museums in other countries.

Julian showed Daniel's friends how to use the microscope, and the young people spent a lot of time taking turns peering through the instrument. They looked at several aquatic insects, spiders, beetles and other small creatures that the scientists had sampled.

The scientific team and villagers exchanged information and knowledge into the early evening hours until they got hungry. They enjoyed a meal, including fish (just as Alina had hoped!), and then they talked some more before going to sleep way past the normal bedtime hour.

The next morning, Alina and Julian again said their farewells. They were sad to leave the village, especially their new friend Daniel, and they were sad to leave the rainforest. But they were also anxious to return home to Lima and tell their parents and classmates all about their adventures.

At school the next week, Alina and Julian met with their classmates for a whole day devoted to describing the specimens and the traps and other equipment that Uncle Pancho lent them. They answered question after question about what the rainforest looked like, what kinds of animals and plants they saw and what were their most exciting moments.

Everyone also wanted to know the most important things that Alina and Julian learned.

"For me, it was how everything in the rainforest works together," Julian answered. "From the plants and soils and rivers and streams that create wildlife habitats to the smallest insects, largest mammals and villagers — everything and everyone has a place, and each species plays several roles. When it's all in balance, we get clean water, good soil, clean air and healthy species."

"I learned how careful we must be not to upset the balance that Julian just described," Alina said. "And I learned about the work that conservation biologists, like my Uncle Pancho, do to make sure the balance is maintained. They get information into the hands of people who make decisions about natural systems. Then, those people have more tools to help protect the environment, including biodiversity."

Mr. Alonso smiled. "Alina and Julian, you make a great team!"

Words to Remember

Amphibians [am-phib-i-ans] are cold-blooded vertebrate animals. (See pages 35-42.)

Aquatic [a-quat-ic] refers to the plants and animals that grow in or live on water. (See pages 21-26.)

Baseline [base-line] is the first information that scientists gather when they go to a site to study biodiversity. (See pages 7-8.)

Biodiversity [bi-o-di-ver-si-ty] is short for biological diversity. It is all living things on Earth. (See pages 2-10.)

Biologists [bi-ol-o-gists] are scientists who study living organisms such as plants, animals, fungi and bacteria. (See pages 7-10.)

Canopy [can-o-py] is the highest layer in a forest. It is formed by the branches and leaves of the tallest trees. In an old or dense forest, the canopy may be very thick, and it may block out most sunlight. (See pages 13-18.)

Cold-blooded [cold blood-ed] means that the body temperature of an animal is about the same as the surrounding air temperature. Reptiles and amphibians are cold-blooded animals. (See pages 36, 42.)

Conservation biologists [con-ser-va-tion bi-ol-o-gists] are scientists who study life and then use the information they gather to help people make decisions about how best to conserve and carefully use natural resources. (See pages 7-10.)

Environments [en-vi-ron-ments] are the physical conditions — forests, rivers, streams, deserts and the like — that surround all living things. Environments play a large part in the ways that living things develop. (See page 8.)

Genes are the elements in all living things that carry hereditary characteristics. Our genes help determine what color our eyes are, how tall we are, the shape of our faces and many other things about us. They make each individual different from all others. (See page 2.)

Habitat [hab-i-tat] is an environment that supports life. Habitats are where plant and animal species live — their "homes." (See pages 13-18.)

Invertebrates [in-ver-te-brates] are animals with no backbones or spinal columns. Insects such as butterflies, flies, bees, beetles and plant bugs are invertebrates. So are earthworms, spiders, scorpions, crabs, crayfishes, lobsters and many more animals. (See pages 28-34.)

Larvae [lar-vae] are young insects, hatched from the egg before they form a cocoon. The larval stage is part of an insect's life cycle. (See page 22.)

Life cycle [cy-cle] is the time that living things spend on Earth. It includes all of the stages that the organism goes through, from birth to death. (See page 21.)

Mammals [mam-mals] are vertebrate animals, most of which have hair. The females produce milk to feed their young. (See pages 51-58.)

Mist net is a device to sample birds and bats. It is a very fine mesh net stretched between two poles. Birds and bats fly into it and are caught, much like in a spider web. (See pages 46-57.)

Monitoring [mon-i-tor-ing] is when scientists sample the same site several times to determine what changes are occurring. (See pages 18, 42.)

pH [p-h] measures the hydrogen level. In water, a pH measurement of 7 means that alkalis and acids in the water are balanced. This is one important way to decide if the water quality is good. (See pages 22, 26.)

Plots are the areas marked off by scientists to study life forms in a specific location. (See pages 14-18.)

Pollinate [pol-li-nate] is what birds, bees, bats and other creatures do when they move a plant's powdery pollen onto a receptive flower. This allows the plant to produce fruit. (See pages 29, 45, 50, 58.)

Predators [pred-a-tors] are animals that hunt other animals for food. (See pages 36, 41.)

Prey is the name given to the animals that are hunted and eaten by predators. (See pages 36, 41, 45.)

Reptiles [rep-tiles] are cold-blooded vertebrates that live on land and in water. (See pages 35-42.)

Sampling [sam-pling] is when scientists gather specimens of animals and plants they are studying in the field. (See pages 7, 32, 40.)

Sign is the evidence that animals leave behind. Scientists can use signs to decide which animals are living in a place, even if they never see the animals. (See pages 52-55.)

A **species** [spe-cies] is a group of living organisms that is separate and distinct from all other groups. A member of a species can successfully reproduce only with another member of that species. (See discussion throughout book.)

Specimens [spec-i-mens] are animals and plants that scientists gather for further study in laboratories and to store in museums. (See description on pages 7-8.)

The **understory** [un-der-stor-y] is the lowest level of plants growing in a forest beneath the mid-size and larger trees. (See page 18.)

Vegetation [veg-e-ta-tion] is another word for plants. (See pages 12-18.)

Vertebrates [ver-te-brates] are animals with backbones or spinal columns. Humans and other mammals are vertebrates. (See pages 36, 42.)

ML

8/02